Tigger's
Little Book of
Bounce

Inspired by A.A. Milne & Illustrated by E.H. Shepard

First published in Great Britain 1999
Printed under the Methuen imprint
by Egmont Children's Books Limited
239 Kensington High Street, London W8 6SA
Copyright © 1999 Michael John Brown, Peter Janson-Smith,
Roger Hugh Vaughan Charles Morgan and Timothy Michael Robinson,
Trustees of the Pooh Properties.
Adapted from *Winnie-the-Pooh* and *The House at Pooh Corner*
text by A.A. Milne and line illustrations by E.H. Shepard
copyright under the Berne Convention
Devised by Charlie Gardner
Book design by Philip Powell
copyright © 1999 Egmont Children's Books Limited

5 7 9 10 8 6 4

ISBN 0 416 19676 4

Printed in Hong Kong

Tigger ... a Very Bouncy Animal
with a way of saying how-do-you-do which
always left your ears full of sand ...

Upword

When I told Winnie-the-Pooh that this part of the
book is called the *Foreword*, he scratched his head and
said that he thought it would be better if I called it the
Forwards, Backwards and Sideways, instead, as Tiggers can
bounce in all directions, not just front ways. And
Tigger — well, Tigger was too busy running around in
circles to think anything much; though he did say he
didn't mind what I called the introduction as long as
I mentioned that this is a happy book about Things
that Tiggers Like Best, and Poohs and Kangas and
Piglets, but not Eeyores — except for the odd place
where Eeyore has trodden on the words. Confused, I

went to see Christopher Robin who had the Very Good Idea to call it the *Upword*, a perfectly positive preamble for this Little Book and the Bouncy Moments contained within it. *Worraworraworraworraworra!*

Make a Grand Entrance

Tigger; a Friendly Tigger, a Grand Tigger, a Large and Helpful Tigger, a Tigger who bounced, if he bounced at all, in just the beautiful way a Tigger ought to bounce.

A Friend Indeed ...

is a friend who opens the door to
you in the middle of the night.

Reflect on your Uniqueness

"Hallo!" said Pooh.
"Hallo!" said Tigger. "I've found somebody just like me. I thought I was the only one of them."

Happy Hour

A stopped clock is always exactly
right twice a day, at least.

Clear Decisions from Clear Honey

Tigger took a large mouthful of honey … and
he looked up at the ceiling with his head on one
side, and made exploring noises with his tongue,
and considering noises, and what-have-we-got-
here noises … and then he said in a very
decided voice:
"Tiggers don't like honey."

Revise your Objectives

"Oh!" said Pooh, and tried to
make it sound Sad and Regretful.
"I thought they liked everything."
"Everything except honey," said Tigger.

Revise your Objectives ... Regularly

"Tiggers don't like haycorns."
"But you said they like everything except honey,"
said Pooh.
"Everything except honey *and* haycorns,"
explained Tigger.

Revise your Objectives ... All the Time!

"But you said," began Pooh, "– you said
that Tiggers liked everything except
honey and haycorns."
"And thistles," said Tigger, who was
now running around in circles with
his tongue hanging out.

Sit on the fence, by all means ...

... but make sure you know which
side to come down on.

Avoid Low Blood Sugar

And Tigger, who had been hiding behind
trees and jumping out on Pooh's shadow
when it wasn't looking, said that Tiggers
were only bouncy before breakfast, and that
as soon as they had had a few haycorns
they became Quiet and Refined.

Changing Rooms

Surprise a friend by doing a
few home improvements for
them while they are out.

Be Larger than Life

"Hallo, Piglet. This is Tigger."
"Oh, is it?" said Piglet, and he edged round to
the other side of the table. "I thought Tiggers
were smaller than that."
"Not the big ones," said Tigger.

First Things First ...

"I've been finding things in the Forest," said
Tigger importantly. "I've found a pooh and a
piglet and an eeyore ...

Second Things Never!

… but I can't find any breakfast."

Strornry Good

Strornry good writers, Tiggers are!

Pooh Bears are *not* strornry
good flyers …

… except when they have a balloon!

A Spoonful of Sugar ...

helps the strengthening medicine go down.

Cupboard Love

The best things in life are like the
forgotten tin of condensed milk ...

waiting to be found at the back of the cupboard.

The Time by Tigger

"I *love* jumping," said Roo. "Let's see
who can jump farthest, you or me."
"*I* can," said Tigger. "But we mustn't
stop now, or we shall be late."
"Late for what?"
"For whatever we want to be in time for,"
said Tigger, hurrying on.

Tall oaks ...

… from little haycorns grow.

Galeforce 8 on the Piglet Scale

Blustery Days should be avoided
by Very Small Animals.

Master the Understatement

"Can Tiggers swim?"
"Of course they can. Tiggers can do
everything."

Rubbish your Competitors

"Can they climb trees better than Pooh?"
asked Roo, stopping under the tallest Pine Tree,
and looking up at it.
"Climbing trees is what they do best,"
said Tigger. "Much better than Poohs."

In at the Deep End

"I'll show you," said Tigger bravely, "and you can sit on my back and watch me." For of all the things which he said Tiggers could do, the only one he felt really certain about suddenly was climbing trees.

Sound Bites

Tablecloths may try to bite you ... when
you're not looking ...

Know your Limits

"I always *said* Tiggers could climb trees."
And for the next ten feet he said:
"Not that it's easy, mind you."
And for the next ten feet he said:
"Of course, there's the coming-down too. Backwards."
And then he said:
"Which will be difficult …"

The Only Way is Up

"... And Tiggers can't climb downwards,
because their tails get in the way, only upwards,
and Tigger forgot about that when we started,
and he's only just remembered ..."

If it Ain't Broke – Don't Fix it.

If it's broken really badly ... don't fix it either.

Time your Exit

"You'll be all right."
"Just wait a moment," said Tigger nervously.
"Small piece of bark in my eye." And he moved
slowly along his branch.
"Come on, it's easy!" squeaked Roo. And
suddenly Tigger found how easy it was.
"Ow!" he shouted as the tree flew past him.
"Look out!" cried Christopher Robin to the others.

Bounce Back from Failure

Eeyore said nothing for a long time. And then
he said: "Is Tigger there?"
Tigger was there feeling bouncy again already.
"Yes," said Christopher Robin. "Tigger's here."
"Well, just thank him for me," said Eeyore.

Learning to Bounce (Beginners)

Find an expert and accompany
them on a *homeward bound*.

I.

2.

3.

Learning to Bounce (Advanced)

If you'd like to be a Kanga it's a good idea
to visit the sandy place on top of the Forest
and try a few practice bounces, first.

Bouncy or Coffy

"He just *is* bouncy," said Piglet,
"and he can't help it." …
"All I did was I coughed," said Tigger.
"He bounced," said Eeyore.
"Well, I sort of boffed," said Tigger.

Know Who You Are

"I am *not* Roo," said Piglet loudly.
"I am Piglet!"
"Yes, dear, yes," said Kanga soothingly.
"And imitating Piglet's voice too!
So clever of him."

The Answer is Blowing in the Wind

At times of crisis, turn to
tried-and-trusted
decision-making tools.

Missage in a Bottle

If you are a Very Small Animal in need of help,
a missage in a bottle is a good idea …

… but only if the larger animal
who finds it can read!

A Broken Mirror Means ...

it's time to get a new one.

Little Pitchers Have Long Ears ...

and so do Little Piglets!

You Can't Lose!

"It's a funny thing about Tiggers,"
whispered Tigger to Roo,
"how Tiggers *never* get lost."
"Why don't they, Tigger?"
"They just don't," explained Tigger.
"That's how it is."

Laughing not Crying

"Tiggers never go on being Sad,"
explained Rabbit. "They get over it with
Astonishing Rapidity."

Red Sky at Night ...

Ernest Shepard's delight.

A.A. MILNE

A.A. Milne, born in 1882, had already made his
name as a dramatist and novelist when *Winnie-the-Pooh* was published in 1926. Milne's stories about
Winnie-the-Pooh were written for his son
Christopher Robin. The characters in the stories
were based upon the real nursery toys which
belonged to Christopher Robin, and their adventures
are set in the Ashdown Forest where the family
lived. The wise words in this little book are to be
found in A.A. Milne's books, *Winnie-the-Pooh* and
The House at Pooh Corner.

E.H. SHEPARD

E. H. Shepard became known as 'The man who drew Pooh'. Born in 1879, Shepard was able to draw well from a very young age. He won a scholarship to the Royal Academy of Arts and became acclaimed as an artist and illustrator. E.H. Shepard's witty and affectionate illustrations of Pooh and his friends from the Hundred Acre Wood are an inseparable part of the appeal of the stories. His illustrations for *Winnie-the-Pooh* and *The House at Pooh Corner* have become classics, recognised all over the world.